HEALTHY LIVING

CONTENTS

About this book

Healthy Living is for teachers of children in Key Stage 2/ Primary 4–7 classes. It contains a series of lively participatory lessons based upon discussion of a full-colour A1 poster, 'Let's get healthy'. This depicts a snapshot view of a range of families living in a block of flats and passers-by in healthy and not so healthy situations, to set a number of potentially sensitive issues within a 'family' context.

The discussion, activities and experiences suggested in this *Resource Bank* book will enable you to:
◆ discover what the children's perceptions are of 'health' and a healthy lifestyle;
◆ build upon this understanding, developing knowledge and skills, and reinforcing positive values and attitudes towards health;
◆ contribute to the science curriculum requirement to learn about the human life cycle;
◆ promote partnership with parents, health professionals and the local community;
◆ contribute to a 'Healthy Schools' programme.

'Good health is treasured. It is the foundation for a good life. Better health for the nation is central to making a better country'.

(*Our Healthier Nation*, July 1997)

INTRODUCTION

About 'healthy living'

The government strategy detailed in *Our Healthier Nation* advocates a 'whole school approach' to personal, social and health education (PSHE) that promotes the raising of self-esteem and the fostering of respect for self and others. These are key messages that should be co-ordinated across the whole curriculum, and are a fundamental part of a Health Promoting School.

Key Stage 2 includes pupils of a very wide age range, from 7 to 11, so the ability and maturity of children in the four year groups will be extremely varied (commonly from National Curriculum Levels 2 to 6 by Year 6). The overall aims of the programme are, therefore, to enable the children to 'be all they can be' at each stage, to take increasing responsibility for their own and others' health, and to begin to appreciate the long- and short-term healthy effects of their present (and future) actions and behaviour.

Other important aims are to broaden their understanding of health from the purely physical 'keep fit and slim' themes to include the value of rest and relaxation; of stress reduction for 'mental health'; of building relationships and partnerships, and to develop skills to resist negative pressures.

Children within this age group are, of course, still very dependent upon their parents and carers, so for a programme to be effective it is essential to gain parental co-operation and to explain the aims so that school work can be reinforced as much as possible at home. Parents may also be able to contribute to the programme in a variety of ways which also provide good role models of adults supporting health.

A list of useful organizations is given on page 4 and a suggested reading list is given on the inside back cover. Neither of these lists is comprehensive, and many of the organizations cited publish other potentially useful material. It is assumed that the content of this book will be supplemented in order to develop a comprehensive and varied programme of activities: for example, discussion of exercise might lead on to considering how the heart works or how our bodies are articulated by muscles and bones.

Sensitive matters

Health education involves discussion of many personal issues, so it is vital to present materials in a way which, while allowing children to discuss things which are relevant to them, protects the confidentiality of both individual pupils and their families.

The 'Let's get healthy' poster facilitates teachers working in this way as it portrays a variety of families with children at all the ages in Key Stage 2. Health issues can be explored through these characters, including discussion of how they might feel and react in certain situations. This protective 'code of confidentiality' approach can be explained to parents, together with information on who they could contact (the school nurse? the deputy head?) if they wish to discuss anything of a confidential nature.

Sex education and the curriculum

Children are entering puberty earlier than ever before. About one in ten girls will have their first period while still at primary school. It is therefore very appropriate when teaching the older children to explain to both girls and boys, in advance, how their bodies will change, and what support will be available for them during this time. Sadly, not all parents and carers are able to provide this information, so schools have a vital role to play in helping children prepare for and cope with these major events. Such teaching in schools will complement that of the parents who are able to talk to their children in this way.

The National Curriculum for Science in England and Wales requires that Key Stage 2 pupils be taught about growth and reproduction in 'the main stages of the human life cycle'. This is an entitlement for all children (including those in Special schools) and parents do not have the right to withdraw their children from this part of the curriculum. At primary level, if any sex education is provided outside the National Curriculum, parents have the right to request that their children be withdrawn. In practice very few do so, especially where they have been actively involved in developing the school's sex education policy.

Nevertheless, schools will find it helpful to explain the context for this part of teaching in the (mandatory) school sex education policy, and to ensure that the school governors, who are legally responsible for the sex education programme overall, are familiar with the rationale, teaching methods and materials to be used. Many schools have found benefits in arranging a health education evening where parents can see previous children's work, learn about the programme aims, view the materials, meet the people involved (including any visitors contributing to the programme), and ask any questions they may have. Some schools have made health materials available to parents, who very much appreciate the chance to update their understanding and discuss the approach being taken. This is especially so if parents have never had any health or sex education themselves, but would like to take up or continue their own role with confidence. On such occasions parents can be reassured that sex education has been shown to be protective and to help young people to delay sexual activity. Without it, children are left vulnerable, open to ridicule and prey to believing dangerous untruths. They also often have false assumptions gained from the media about what is 'normal' behaviour. The human life cycle section of this book would be very appropriate for a Year 6 class after their work on life cycles in Year 5.

The Scottish National Guidelines 5–14 on Health Education cover relationships, well-being and self-knowledge in Primary 4–6 and 'sexuality and sexual responsibility' from Primary 7. In the Northern Ireland Curriculum, pubertal change is included in the Key Stage 2 Programme of Study, but is non-statutory.

Parenting skills
There has been a renewed focus upon the importance of parenting, with several government initiatives to promote parenting skills. Many skills such as understanding the needs of young children, listening, helping, teaching, caring and taking responsibility, can be developed at primary school in various contexts. Other planned activities can be seen to value parents and their skills, and to raise their self-esteem.

Other considerations
As always, teachers will be aware of the need to be sensitive to the cultural and religious beliefs of pupils and their families, and to take care to include appropriate activities, and examples in the teaching. The empty flat on the A1 poster allows children to decide for themselves the nature of the family that might come to live there, and to explore what their health needs might be.

Children enjoy learning about health, and can be motivated to extend the work into all areas of the formal and informal curriculum, which generates interest both inside and outside school.

Preparing to use the poster
The 'Let's get healthy' poster enables you to explore health issues by considering the lifestyles of five families living in a block of flats:

Flat 1: Brian and Ann Tyler, expecting a new baby, and Holly, aged 3.
Flat 2: Mrs Edith Wilson, aged 80, recently bereaved.
Flat 3: Janice and Mark, a young couple in their 20s.
Flat 4: Jeff and Angela Nicol, with 10½ year old twins, Carli and Tom.
Flat 5: An empty flat – used in 'Healthy Living Review' activity on page 32.
Flat 6: Pat and Steve Adams, with Mel (5), Emma (8) and Michael (13).

Some of the characters are used in specific activities (see 'Healthy Living Review', page 32), but you can devise relationships (for example, whether or not they are stepfamilies) to suit the background of your class.

The black and white side of the poster shows 'The human life cycle', but with a social context added to the more usual reproductive model. This enables you to focus upon major changes for children such as starting and leaving school, as well as the physical and emotional aspects of puberty.

LET'S LOOK AT THE POSTER

GROUP SIZE AND ORGANIZATION
Whole class sitting facing the poster.
DURATION
About 30 minutes.
LEARNING OBJECTIVES
To become familiar with the 'Let's get healthy' poster. To explore the things that people can do to become and stay healthy. To understand that places, people and behaviour can all have an effect upon our health. To start to develop a vocabulary for communicating about health.

YOU WILL NEED
The 'Let's get healthy' poster.
Green and red stick-on spots – about 20 of each.

DISCUSSION QUESTIONS
Ask the class:
◆ *What do you think people mean by 'being healthy'?*
◆ *How can we tell if someone is healthy or not?*
Explain that over the next lessons you'll be finding out about things that can help us to be healthy, and about some things that may have the opposite effect.

Ask the children to look carefully at the poster. Explain that the people shown on it will help you to focus upon different ways of keeping healthy (if you wish you could introduce some of the 'characters' whose details are given around the edge of the picture.) Can they pick out, giving their reasons and discussing:
◆ *Which people in the poster are doing things that*

INTRODUCTION

will help to keep them healthy? (Jogging, cycling, gardening, using the zebra crossing, walking, cleaning teeth, washing hands, eating, and so on.)

◆ *Which people are doing things which might harm their health?* (Unsafe cyclist, footballer near road, smoker, child leaning over balcony, child near flex of iron, and so on.)

◆ *Which people are helping other people to be healthy?* (Midwife, girl with flowers, police, parents, lifeguard, older children, and so on.)

◆ *Which people might make someone else unhealthy?* (Offer of cigarettes, bad cyclist, car exhaust, and so on.)

◆ *Which places or things can they see which might be dangerous to health?* (Road, waste tip, flex from iron, sharp tools, cigarettes, and so on.)

◆ *Which places or things might be helpful to health?* (Zebra crossing, allotment, swimming pool, food, drink, and so on.)

When you have agreed upon healthy and unhealthy activities and situations, ask volunteers to stick green spots on the 'good health' examples, and red spots on the potentially damaging ones. Explain to the children that these will be discussed in future lessons, and ask them to reflect upon what they have done.

◆ *Have you learned anything you didn't know before?*

◆ *What more would you like to learn about how to keep yourselves and others healthy?*

Such a reflective, plenary session should be included at the end of each activity or section.

EXTENSION QUESTIONS

◆ *What might this scene look like when it gets dark?*

◆ *How might the scene appear in the winter?*

◆ *Are there different health problems or opportunities then, in the dark, or in winter?*

USEFUL ADDRESSES

Education Development Service, Warwickshire Education Services, Manor Hall, Sandy Lane, Leamington Spa CV32 6RD. Tel: 01926 413775

TACADE (The Advisory Council on Alcohol & Drug Education), 1 Hulme Place, The Crescent, Salford, Greater Manchester, M5 4QA. Tel: 0161 745 8925

British Heart Foundation, 14 Fitzhardinge Street, London, W1H 4DH.

Health Education Authority, Trevelyan House, 30 Great Peter St, London SW1 2HW. Tel: 0171 222 5300

Brook Advisory Centres (Publications), 165 Grays Inn Road, London WC1X 8UD. Tel: 0171 833 8488

Health Education Board for Scotland, Woodburn House, Canaan Lane, Edinburgh EH10 4SG. Tel: 0131 447 8044

Health Promotion Agency for Northern Ireland, 18 Ormeau Avenue, Belfast BT2 8HS. Tel: 01232 311611

Health Promotion Wales, Ffynnon-las, Ty Glas Avenue, Llanishen, Cardiff CF4 5DZ. Tel: 01222 752222

KIDSCAPE, 152 Buckingham Palace Road, London SW1W 9TR. Tel: 0171 730 3300

Birmingham Advisory & Support Service, (BASS) Teacher Support Section, Martineau Centre, Balden Road, Harborne, Birmingham B32 2EH. Tel: 0121 428 1167 x 279

Council for Environmental Education, University of Reading, London Road, Reading RG1 5AQ. Tel: 0118 975 6061

Schools Education Unit, Renslade House, Bonhay Road, Exeter EX4 3AY. Tel: 01392 667272

District Health Promotion Links
Contact your District Health Authority or the Health Education Authority for details.

Local Education Authority Your LEA may have a Health Education Co-ordinator who can assist you. It may also issue sex education guidelines for schools.

EXERCISE AND REST

X-ERCISE FILE

GROUP SIZE AND ORGANIZATION
Whole class, then in groups of four or five, then whole class.
DURATION
About 30 minutes.
LEARNING OBJECTIVES
To explore the reasons why people exercise, and to promote positive attitudes to exercise.

YOU WILL NEED
The 'Let's get healthy' poster, large sheets of (flip chart) paper, marker pens, Blu-Tack.

WHAT TO DO
Ask the class to think about what people mean when they talk about 'getting enough exercise'. Some experts think that children in the UK now are not getting enough exercise. What do you think? What kind of exercise did children in the past get? (Many had long distances to walk to school and back.) What is meant by 'today's sedentary lifestyle' ('sedentary' comes from the Latin *sedere*, to sit)?

Refer to the 'Let's get healthy' poster. What sorts of exercise are the people in the poster doing? (Cycling, walking, gardening, swimming, football, dancing, skipping, and so on.) Give each group a sheet of paper. Ask the children to discuss and write (or draw) all the reasons they can think of for why people exercise.

Go round the groups encouraging them to think of a variety of reasons. You might like to suggest or reinforce that regular exercise is needed several times a week, to increase strength, stamina and suppleness. Doing exercise you like is fun and pleasurable, and develops teamwork and friendships. It also:
◆ Strengthens all body muscles and keeps bodies flexible and agile.
◆ Strengthens heart muscle (vital for reducing heart disease – hearts beat faster, measured by the pulse rate).
◆ Makes the heart and lungs work efficiently – they need exercise too! Better blood circulation takes more oxygen to all parts of the body, including the brain – people can think and concentrate better.
◆ Lowers blood pressure, so reducing risk of strokes.
◆ Gives a person more energy, making them 'bright eyed and bushy tailed', rather than having an inactive 'couch potato' feeling.

◆ Reduces stress and worries, as during exercise the body makes natural tranquillizers (endorphins) with a calming effect, so exercise helps body and mind – and it's fun!

A 'fat' person who takes regular exercise can be much fitter than a 'thin' person who takes no exercise (and exercise plus sensible eating can help people to lose weight).

Ask the groups to display their sheets and compare their ideas. What is the most popular reason for exercising? How many different reasons are there all together? Stress that exercise strengthens our hearts, and add this to the lists if necessary (and in future link to PE sessions taking pulse rates – with digital pulse meters if possible – before and after normal exercise activities). Explain that becoming hot, puffed and perspiring is a necessary sign of sufficient exercise, and should happen several times a week.

Discuss what may happen if people don't get enough exercise. How can we as a class help people to get more exercise?

ASSESSMENT
Assess with the class the practicalities of their ideas for more exercise and implement them if possible. Could they help children in younger classes with throwing, catching and other games?

IDEAS FOR DISPLAY
Set up an ongoing display. Ask the children to collect pictures of as many different races and ages of people doing as many different kinds of exercise as possible, with each activity suitably labelled. These should include everyday exercise as well as Olympic and Paralympic efforts and professional sports people!

IDEAS FOR DIFFERENTIATION
Refer less able pupils back to the poster and ask them to list or draw two or three of the exercise activities shown. They could then add one reason why the people they have chosen might do these activities.

More able pupils could use the information from your group discussion to detail as many reasons as possible for exercising, and try to give some explanation of the physiology involved (blood circulation and pressure and so on.)

EXTENSION WORK
For homework, ask the children to keep an exercise diary for a week and count up how many out of breath activities they did. A focus upon 'perspiring' can lead to work on the necessity to wash or shower regularly, and at least to wash hands after taking part in

EXERCISE AND REST

games or other strenuous activity.

Some children could concentrate upon one particular form of sport or exercise, and research its history, or find out which sports are popular in which countries, or look for record breaking achievements using the *Guinness Book of Records*, CD-Roms, or the National Grid for Learning *Wired for Health*.

EVERYBODY CAN DO SOMETHING!

GROUP SIZE AND ORGANIZATION
Whole class, then in pairs or small groups, then whole class.
DURATION
About 30 minutes.
LEARNING OBJECTIVES
To promote understanding that while everyone can enjoy a range of exercise activities, certain body shapes and skills are better suited to some sports than others. •
To identify present strengths, and future possibilities.
To accept difference.

YOU WILL NEED
Pictures of a range of sportspeople (possibly from the last activity) — marathon runners, sprinters, high jumpers, basketball players, swimmers, and so on, and a male or female football team showing various sized players, a copy of photocopiable page 8 for each child.

WHAT TO DO
Ask the children to look at the pictures.
◆ *Are the people all the same size and shape?*
◆ *When a football team lines up for kick-off, are they all the same?*
◆ *Why might the coach have selected a range of people?*
Discuss the many different skills a football team needs — running, dodging, kicking, throwing, heading, accurate passing, judging distance, and so on. Suggest that this demonstrates that while we can all do some activities, different body shapes and sizes are particularly good at certain things.

Ask the children to work in pairs or small groups. Give every child a copy of the photocopiable page 8. Allow a few minutes for them to read it. Then get the children to ask each other about their favourite exercise or sport, and to fill in the sheet together. In a round, ask everyone to tell of one exercise activity that they enjoy doing themselves.

ASSESSMENT
Do the class as a whole take part in a range of different exercise activities and understand that different individuals are better suited to different activities?

IDEAS FOR DIFFERENTIATION
For less able children, blank out the last sections of the photocopiable page and ask the children to draw a picture of themselves exercising in the empty space.

More able children could write the names of athletes who excel in the various activities on the right (eg, Steve Redgrave, rowing) and comment on their physique and body shape.

EXTENSION WORK
Less confident children could select a picture of their favourite athlete or sportsperson and write about their skills, and why they admire them.

What skills and sports are the children asking for? How could such training be arranged? How might the school Sports Day be extended to include a wider range of events to give different children a chance to succeed?

Children who use the local sports or leisure centre could find out about all the activities, their times and costs, with a personal endorsement of those they have tried themselves, and an offer to help those who would like to try it.

VISITORS
The class might decide to ask a professional from the centre (or a local sportsperson) to come to talk to them about a particular sport, local facilities, special events, or holiday fitness or coaching schemes. How are families catered for?

RESOURCE BANK

HEALTHY LIVING

EXERCISE AND REST

REST A WHILE

GROUP SIZE AND ORGANIZATION
Whole class, then in pairs.
DURATION
About 30 minutes.
LEARNING OBJECTIVES
To develop a vocabulary for describing exercise.
To understand the importance of relaxation and sleep.

YOU WILL NEED
Photocopiable page 9 for each child, blank sheets of paper, recording of relaxing 'mood music'.

SENSITIVITIES
Some children stay up very late, to the detriment of their health. They may boast about how late they go to sleep. Whilst acknowledging that different families and individuals have different needs, it is important to stress the positive health value of adequate sleep, especially for growing children (the growth hormone is mainly produced during sleep). Primary school children ideally need about ten hours of sleep every night.

WHAT TO DO
Give out photocopiable page 9 and the blank sheets. Ask individuals to read out the words in the five sections of the word exercise. Then ask:
◆ *What do you feel like after exercising?* (Happy, but hot, sweaty and tired. Time for a wash or shower, and to cool down and relax or sleep.)
◆ *How important do you think sleep is for growing bodies?* (Very important as part of the growing process.)
◆ *What happens if we don't get enough sleep?* (We become tired, irritable and can't think properly.)

Working in pairs, ask each child to add some words to the inner circle on the sheet, and draw or write in the centre how they like to relax. Play some soothing music during this time.

ASSESSMENT
Ask the children what they learned from this lesson, and whether it has made them think of sleep in a more positive way. Do they realize now that sleep is a health issue? Do their attitudes indicate that they think it is 'babyish' to go to bed 'early', and sophisticated and adult to 'stay up late'?

IDEAS FOR DIFFERENTIATION
Less confident readers could use two blank sheets headed 'Rest a while' to draw a picture of an active, jolly person who has enough sleep and a tired grumpy one who has not. Able children could add as many words as possible to the word circle and use them to make a rap poem, 'Word exercise'.

EXTENSION WORK
For homework children could keep a 'sleep chart' for themselves for a week and calculate, with family help, how many hours sleep they get, and how many they feel they need. Do they match up? Children could draw 24-hour clocks showing the sleep patterns of babies, toddlers, children and adults, and comment upon the differences.

Suggest that Michael Adams (in Flat 6 on the 'Let's get healthy' poster) never gets enough sleep. Ask the class to suggest why this might be:
◆ *Is Michael not going to bed when asked, reading in bed or watching TV? How would you try to convince him that sleep is important? What would you advise him to do?* Children could then decide on the beneficial effects if their advice was acted upon, and display these in drawings and writings about Michael 'before' and 'after' getting enough sleep.

SLEEP PATTERNS (24 HOUR CLOCKS)

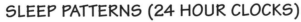

Time asleep

Baby

Noon

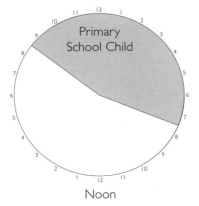

Primary School Child

Noon

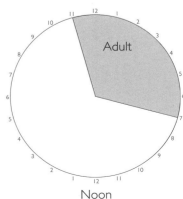

Adult

Noon

Name ——————————————— Date ———————————————

Everybody can do something!

Find an exercise you like doing...

skipping

table tennis

disco dancing

keep fit

line-dancing

catching sticks!

Our names are ——————— and ——————— .

Our favourite exercises at the moment are

———————————————————————

——————————————————————— .

When we are doing them we feel

——————————————————————— .

We like doing them because

——————————————————————— .

We think everybody should exercise because ———————————————

——————————————————————— .

We would like to increase our skills in

———————————————————————

——————————————————————— .

We could get help from ———————————

——————————————————————— .

Signed ———————————

———————————

People come in many different shapes and sizes. Future prospects...

Long arms?

Basketball and swimming

Strong legs?

Running fast, sprinting

Long and lean?

Long-distance running

Strong upper body?

Throwing and rowing

Good stamina?

Cycling, swimming and long-distance running

Good agility?

Good eye-hand co-ordination?

Tennis, badminton, football...

Good at jumping up?

High jump, rugby, speed swimming

Football, gymnastics, badminton

Name _____   Date _____

Exercise and... rest a while...

Words for warming up

Words for doing

stretching, slow jogs, running on the spot, jumping, skipping, lifting, pushing, bouncing, leaping, sprinting, racing, panting, puffing, perspiring, slowing, stopping, cooling, washing, showering, resting, relaxing, sleeping ZZZZZZZ

Your words

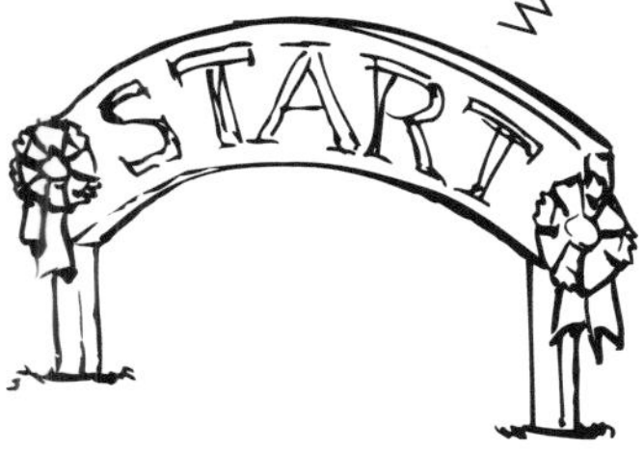

START

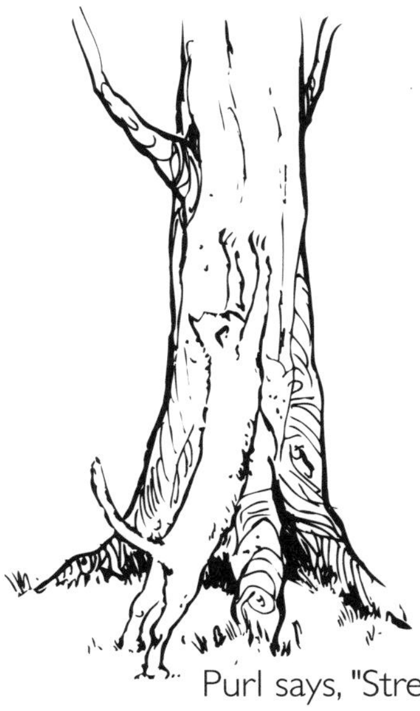

Purl says, "Stretching is good."

Words for feeling

Words for relaxing

Words for recovering

EAT FOR HEALTH

A HANDFUL OF HEALTH

GROUP SIZE AND ORGANIZATION
Whole class, small groups, finally whole class.
DURATION
About 45 minutes, plus time each day for about seven days to 'water' the beans.
LEARNING OBJECTIVES
To promote fruit and vegetable eating and growing.

YOU WILL NEED
The 'Let's get healthy' poster, an A4 sheet of paper for each child, lots of pictures of fruit and vegetables cut out of magazines and leaflets – a pile of these for each group. For the experiment: mung beans (from health food shops), six jam jars, J-cloths (or equivalent), elastic bands, dessert spoons and water.

WHAT TO DO
Refer to the poster:
◆ *What are the Adams family growing in their allotment?* (Apples, strawberries, runner beans, courgettes, spinach, tomatoes, potatoes, herbs.) List these on the board. Tell the children that herbs can be used to flavour dishes instead of salt (which can cause high blood pressure).
◆ *Do any of your families grow other vegetables?* (Add these to the list.)
◆ *Might it be possible to grow things on a smaller scale than a whole allotment?* (How about tomatoes in a growbag, or growing bean sprouts on a windowsill?)

Each group can start growing bean sprouts by putting a heaped dessertspoonful of mung beans in the bottom of a jam jar and covering it with a square of J-cloth held in place with an elastic band.

Water is then poured onto the beans through the J-cloth, left for five minutes, then drained off by inverting the jam jar. This process is repeated every day until the sprouts are ready for eating in six to seven days.

Working in groups, now ask each child to draw round their hand on the A4 paper, and to think of five sorts of fruit and vegetables that they like to eat, and to draw or stick a picture of each one above a finger or thumb. Get them to write on the finger why they like their choice. Next ask them to write on the rest of the hand as many fruit and vegetable dishes or drinks they can think of – celery soup, baked apples, coleslaw, tomato ketchup, banana milk shake, stir-fried bean sprouts, and so on. The children can compare their 'handfuls' and display them.

crunchy
soft & sweet
flavour
juicy
tasty

Tomato soup
Sweetcorn
Cauliflower cheese
Baked apples

GROWING MUNG BEANS

Mung beans

Bean sprouts

EAT FOR HEALTH

TAKE 5

Explain that everyone is advised to protect themselves (from cancers and heart disease) by having this handful of at least five portions of fruit and vegetables every day. (Most people only have three or less.)

ASSESSMENT

How well have the children understood the wide range of possible fruit and vegetable choices? Can they suggest ways in which everyone could increase the amount of fruit and vegetables eaten per day or week?

IDEAS FOR DIFFERENTIATION

Less able children could draw the five chosen items over their fingers and sort the pile of pictures into two groups of fruit or vegetables.

EXTENSION WORK

For homework, let each child take a large sheet of paper home on which to draw seven hand shapes and fill in what they had every day for a week.

IDEAS FOR DISPLAY

Small groups could devise a 'promotion' for a particular fruit or vegetable dish, designing a logo and a slogan (as a competition?). Different fruit and vegetables could be arranged and presented with a description of their texture, smell, and (if appropriate) taste. Presentation and aesthetic quality of food is important in making choices. If a tasting session is allowed, great care must be taken with hygiene, washing of hands, and the teacher's awareness of diabetics or any food allergies.

FOOD BALANCING CHOICES

GROUP SIZE AND ORGANIZATION
Whole class, then eight groups, then whole class.
DURATION
About 45 minutes.
LEARNING OBJECTIVES
To understand the need for balance and variety in our diets. To make healthy food choices.

YOU WILL NEED

A flip chart and marker pen or chalkboard and chalk, a very large sheet of paper with a 1m diameter circle drawn on (as in the illustration on page 12), lots of pictures of different foods, cut from magazines and leaflets, to include many examples of the five groups explained below, Blu-Tack, a copy of photocopiable page 15 for each child.

SENSITIVITIES

One clearly visible health issue is that of being overweight, and many children worry about being teased about this. There is also concern about the growing incidence of anorexia, so 'fatness' should not be a main focus for this age group. Teachers will need to be aware of children with food allergies or with special dietary needs such as diabetics. Some children may be vegetarians or have cultural or religious reasons for not eating certain foods. Such children may well be 'food experts' and able to contribute much to class discussion. Make sure that the children realize that 'diet' refers to what we eat, not just to the loss of weight.

WHAT TO DO

Ask the class to think of all the reasons why we eat and drink. Write the answers on the board. (Because we are hungry; we like eating; to give us energy; to enable us to grow; to have strong bones and teeth; to heal wounds; to resist diseases by keeping our 'germ busting' immune system in good order; to prevent certain diseases such as those caused by a lack of vitamins.) We also eat and drink for social and cultural reasons. These occasions keep us in good social and mental health.

In this country we are fortunate enough to have sufficient food, so have many choices about what we eat. Explain that to keep our bodies physically healthy we need to eat a variety of foods, but that the amounts of different foods we eat in the long term does matter, and it is very important to get the balance right. In simple terms we all need to eat more fruit, vegetables, and starchy foods, and less fat, sugar and salt.

Ask the children what groups of foods they have heard of. These will probably be proteins, carbohydrates, fats, minerals and vitamins. Explain that there is a different way of grouping the foods which health and nutrition experts think will help us all to make good food choices. ('Carbohydrates', for example, covers beneficial starchy foods (such as bread, cereals and rice), as well as not so useful sugar in all its forms.)

Show the class the paper circle. Talk about the labels on each section and how much of the food in the section should go to make up a 'balanced diet' to eat if possible every day (including 'snacks'). As you discuss

EAT FOR HEALTH

BALANCED CHOICES

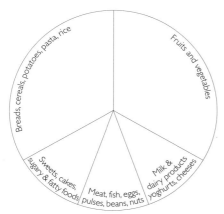

Breads, cereals, potatoes, pasta, rice

Fruits and vegetables

Sweets, cakes, sugary & fatty foods

Meat, fish, eggs, pulses, beans, nuts

Milk & dairy products yoghurts, cheeses

each section, ask individuals to select pictures of the appropriate foods and stick them on with Blu-Tack. They will find they have much more space in some sections than others, emphasizing the relative balance.

Section 1: Breads of all kinds, to give us helpful starchy carbohydrate (for energy) and fibre. The extra fibre in wholemeal versions acts like a sponge, helping to move food down the long tubes of our digestive system. Starchy foods should make up about one third of a meal (but not if fried or loaded with fat).

Section 2: Fruit and vegetables for fibre, vitamins and other health promoting chemicals. Fruit and vegetables should make up one third of a meal.

Section 3: Milk and dairy foods give us calcium (for strong teeth and bones), protein (for growth) and vitamins. We should eat moderate amounts of these foods. Low fat versions are best and have more calcium than the full fat ones.

Section 4: Meat, fish, beans, lentils (pulses), nuts and eggs give us protein, minerals including iron (for blood) and vitamins. We should try to eat mainly low fat versions.

Section 5: Sweets, snack foods, fats and sugar provide fat and sugar for energy. We should eat only small amounts of these. (Sad news?!) Too much fat can lead to heart disease and strokes (and being overweight). Sugar does not provide other nutrients, and can lead to dental decay (see 'Smile please' on pages 13–14). All the things provided by this group can be obtained from the other food groups with less harmful side effects.

Now the good news! This doesn't mean that we should *never* eat these foods, but that they should *not* be the 'main course' of the day every day, nor grazed on all day long.

Now ask the children to work in eight groups. Give each child a copy of photocopiable page 15. Ask seven of the groups to discuss the lunch or picnic box options, choosing three items for the box, plus a drink, which will provide a balanced meal. Tell the one remaining group to select the least healthy choice they can! Tell the children to draw their chosen items into the boxes and be prepared to explain their choices to one other group.

Display the seven 'balanced choice' boxes shown below in a row, as one person's lunches for a week. Now ask them to imagine 52 such rows: lunches for a year. What might be the health differences between such a person and another that had 7 × 52 = 364 lunches from the least healthy box?

ONE WEEK'S LUNCHES... HEALTHY CHOICES... X 52 = 1 YEAR OF HEALTHY LUNCHES

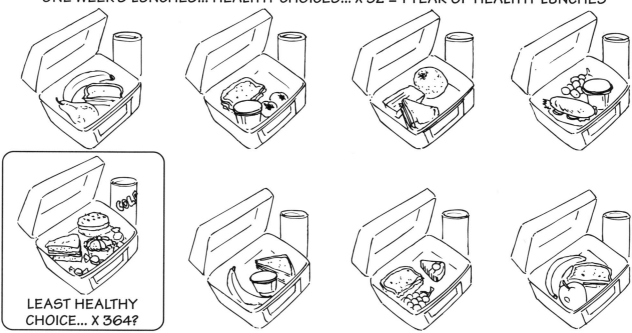

LEAST HEALTHY CHOICE... X 364?

RESOURCE BANK

HEALTHY LIVING

EAT FOR HEALTH

ASSESSMENT

How accurate are the children in placing foods in the appropriate sections? Have they understood about the relative proportions of the groups, and that while no food is 'bad' food, some is much more beneficial?

Ask what the children think is the most important thing they have learned today. How could they explain this to others? (An assembly?)

IDEAS FOR DIFFERENTIATION

Using photocopiable page 15, less able children could colour in all the fruit and vegetables. More able children could assess the fat and sugar content of each item and invent a system for identifying high fat and sugar foods.

EXTENSION WORK

To be effective this work must relate to actual eating! Children could help to organize healthy options for the school tuck shop, and the school could liaise with the dinner service, if necessary, to instigate healthy options, or a 'traffic light' system of coding to help children make healthy choices.

VISITORS

The class might like to find out about global projects (eg, Farm Africa) to help people grow their own food, or invite someone from Oxfam to come and talk about their food programmes and how the class could help to raise money for them.

SMILE PLEASE!

GROUP SIZE AND ORGANIZATION
Whole class, then in six groups, finally whole class.
DURATION
About 30 minutes for each of two sessions, one week apart.
LEARNING OBJECTIVES
To gain knowledge and skills for dental health. To experience the effects of acids on 'eggshell teeth'.

YOU WILL NEED

A poster of a giant mouth (optional – may be available from a local dental surgery), seven half eggshells from boiled (to eliminate the salmonella risk) eggs, seven jam jars or other transparent containers, pencils, cotton, Blu-Tack, labels, six fruit and other drinks such as 'High juice' lemon, orange squash, cola, tap water; flip chart and marker pen or chalkboard and chalk.

SENSITIVITIES

Children in this age group will be beginning to lose their deciduous (baby) teeth of eight incisors, four canines and eight molars, and their permanent teeth will be growing down, usually in this order:

Permanent Teeth	Age of eruption	Use
Incisors	lower 6–8 upper 7–9	For cutting
Canines	lower 9–10 upper 11–12	For tearing
Pre-molars	9–12	For crushing and chewing
First molar (comes behind the last milk molar)	6–7	For crushing and chewing
Second molar	11–13	For crushing and chewing
Third molar (wisdom tooth)	17–21	For crushing and chewing

N.B. Every school should know how to contact emergency dental care in the event of an accident.

WHAT TO DO

Erupting teeth are particularly vulnerable to **acid attack**, so the following experiment is very relevant. Euromonitor research showed that 'In the UK we consume on average 41 litres of cola, 51 litres of non-cola fizzy drinks and 25 litres of fruit drinks per head (and per tooth!) per year.' Show the children the mouth poster, if available, and talk about the children's different types and numbers of teeth.

◆ *Why are smiles important?* (We use smiles as greetings, to show friendship, because we're happy and having fun.)
◆ *What else do we use our mouths for?* (To speak, sing, play musical instruments, suck, blow, kiss and eat.)
◆ *Which part of our mouths do we use in eating?* (Lips, tongue, gums and teeth.)
◆ *What could damage our teeth?* (Accidents, and our food!)
◆ *How can food damage our teeth?*

To understand this, the children need to know that the outside surfaces of teeth are made of a very hard substance called **enamel**. Underneath is a softer layer of **dentine**. Enamel, though very hard, is easily dissolved by chemicals called 'acids': vinegar, lemon juice, in cola, the 'fizz' in soft drinks, even vitamin C. To demonstrate a similar effect to that of acids on teeth, set up the following experiment on eggshells, using them as 'pretend' tooth enamel.

List the drinks to be tested on the board and

EAT FOR HEALTH

explain that they have been diluted as recommended or are straight from the can. (Milk could be used for a few days if the jam jar is kept in a fridge.) Ask how can we make it a 'fair' test, so that we know it is the acid in the drink having the effect, if any. (Use tap water or a drink with no acid in it as a control.)

Divide the class into six groups and tell each one to set up a jar as shown in the diagram. Each group can test one drink or set up the control.

In your next session, help the groups to describe what has happened to their shell. Any pitting or crumbling of the surface indicates acid attack. Put all the jars and eggshells in a row so the results can be easily compared.

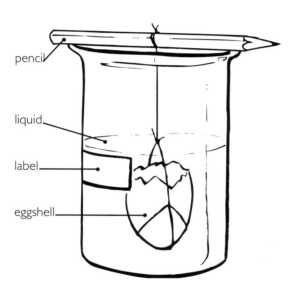

pencil

liquid

label

eggshell

Something in these drinks has had an effect upon the eggshells and the same substances will be able to attack the enamel of our teeth. So, we need to read the label on drinks to find out if they contain acid. Why should we also look to see if they contain added sugar?

The children also need to understand that our teeth are covered with a sticky layer called **plaque** which contains millions of bacteria too small to see. These bacteria love sugar and turn it into acid. Write this on the board:

*Teeth + plaque + sugar = acid   attack enamel on
                                                    teeth   dental decay*

So each time we eat or drink sugary foods, the enamel on our teeth will come under attack, but the good news (at last!) is that the saliva (spit) in our mouths can neutralize the acid and rebuild the damaged enamel. Brilliant!

Ask: What could we all do to lessen acid attack so

that our permanent teeth last permanently? Ideas can be listed on the flip chart and should include:
◆ Get rid of the plaque. Brush teeth really well (with a fluoride toothpaste) at least twice a day. (Plaque can build up rapidly.)
◆ Keep sugar intake to meal times. Eat starchy and sugary foods only at mealtimes.
◆ Keep acid away. Don't drink many acidic, sugary or fizzy drinks, especially between meals. Always drink through a straw to keep the drink away from the teeth. Look at drink labels to see what is in them. Always dilute concentrated drinks properly. Drink milk or water (weak tea or coffee?) instead of just sweet drinks.
◆ Take your teeth for servicing. Have a check with a dentist at least once a year.

ASSESSMENT
How far have the children grasped the idea of the two sources of acid attack on teeth (one from chemicals – acids – already in some drinks, the other from acids made by the action of mouth bacteria on sugar)? Can they explain what would happen to the teeth of a child who sucked sweets and drank acidic drinks all day long ('joined up eating')? What chance would his/her saliva have to rebuild enamel?

IDEAS FOR DIFFERENTIATION
More able children could look at the labels on the tested drinks and make a comparison chart of acid and sugar content to add to their results.

EXTENSION WORK
Children could collect pictures of smiles and make a 'mile of smiles' frieze to keep everyone cheerful. Others could make large models of individual teeth, and a huge toothbrush, and demonstrate how to clean all the surfaces. Molars and premolars can be made from cube-shaped tissue boxes, while canines and incisors can be made from tights packets. Some children could find out how much different toothpastes and brushes cost, and work out dental costs per week. What is the cost of *not* looking after your teeth? Some could undertake a survey of television commercials that promote sugary food and devise counteracting ones promoting 'safe' eating and drinking.

VISITORS
The class might invite a dental health promotion officer, an oral hygienist or a dentist to come and explain about orthodontic work and the best method of brushing teeth and gums.

14 RESOURCE BANK HEALTHY LIVING

Name ————————————   Date ————————————

Food balancing choices

Drink of...?
skimmed milk
cola
orange juice
squash

dates

grapes

wholemeal
sandwiches with
egg and tomato

iced bun

lean ham roll

sausage rolls

cherry
tomatoes

white bread
sandwiches with
butter and jam

samosa

pitta bread with
sweetcorn and
sardines in tomato

crisps

apple

cherries

sweets

celery
sticks

chocolate bar

low fat, extra
fruit yoghurt

pizza with low fat cheese,
tomatoes and pepper

PHOTOCOPIABLE

RESOURCE
BANK

KEEPING OURSELVES SAFE

TURN AROUND THE TIP

GROUP SIZE AND ORGANIZATION
Whole class, then in pairs, then in fours, then pairs and finally the whole class.
DURATION
45 minutes.
LEARNING OBJECTIVES
To find out how the physical environment affects our health.

YOU WILL NEED
The poster 'Let's get healthy', sheets of A4 paper and scissors for each pair, red stick-on spots, addresses of the local newspaper and conservation groups.

WHAT TO DO
Show the children the poster with the original green and red spotted areas.
◆ *Are there any areas that are especially dangerous to health, and might need two or more red spots on?* (The road and the waste tip qualify.)
◆ *Who is responsible for them?* (It depends upon who owns them, but most likely the local council.)

Suggest that the families in the flats are fed up with having the tip so near their homes, so they have invited their local councillor, Mrs Shirwar, to a meeting, so that they can show her the tip and explain what they would like done about it.

FOLDED PAPER

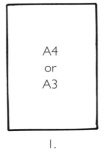

1.

2.

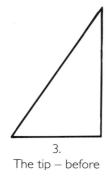

3.
The tip – before

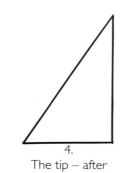

4.
The tip – after

*Fellowship Flats
Greenroad
Cryton*

*Dear Mrs Shirwar,
Thank you so much for coming to see us. We would be grateful if you could tell your other councillors about our worries.
If you remember these were . . . . .*

LOOKING AT THE POSTER
Are there any areas round the flats that they could tidy up themselves (as a 'goodwill' gesture) before she comes? (The wheely bin area, the hall, the allotment shed and gate, for example.)
◆ *How far should we all be responsible for our own immediate areas?*
◆ *How could they be made more attractive?* (Drawings of the area tidied up [with flower tubs?] could be stuck over the poster later.)
◆ *Why do you think the tip area is damaging to health?* (in the broadest sense, ie, injurious to mental 'comfort'.)
Ideas might include: children climbing on the tip having accidents; there could be dangerous chemicals leaking out of old cans; the tip smells awful; it attracts people who are noisy and frightening; it is not well lit at night and so seems threatening.

Working in pairs again, ask the children to fold and cut the A4 sheet of paper diagonally in half. Ask them to draw on one triangle a rubbish tip similar to the one on the poster labelled 'before', and on the other triangle what it could look like 'after' being cleared and planted with shrubs, with a seat and waste bin and so on, as a 'conservation corner'. These can be displayed in pairs.

ASSESSMENT
Are the children concerned about the quality of their environment? How far are they aware of the risks of playing on dangerous areas? Do children understand the role and powers of councillors and local community groups and the value of discussing problems together and coming to a consensus for action? Is this reflected in a class or school council?

RESOURCE BANK

HEALTHY LIVING

IDEAS FOR DIFFERENTIATION

In fours, more able children could share their ideas in relation to the poster, decide which are the best ones, and write these in the form of a letter to the councillor, explaining the problem and asking for the site to be cleared and levelled.

The children's letters could be displayed and assessed for effectiveness in getting a response. They should be polite but should stress that the problem is urgent.

EXTENSION WORK

Ask the children:

◆ *Do you know of any 'turn around' projects undertaken in this area?*

◆ *How could we find this out? Has the local newspaper reported any recently?*

◆ *Are there any parts of the school grounds that might be turned into a nature trail, conservation area or allotment?*

◆ *Who could help?* These discussions could lead to children-led ongoing projects involving local groups. A team of 'litter bugs' could organize keeping the school and grounds litter free, and recruit help from other classes. Others could find out and report to the rest of the class about local refuse collection policy and services, facilities for disposing of large items, recycling bottles, cans, paper, clothes, old batteries and so on.

On an enlarged street map of the local area, children could identify places helping communities to stay healthy (GPs, clinics, pharmacists, recreation centres), and discuss how to get to and from them in safety. Dangerous areas, railway lines, rivers, building sites and so on could be designated 'no go' areas and the reasons discussed.

VISITORS

A road safety or ROSPA officer could be invited to the school to support work on safety at home, and on the roads.

The concept of **sustainable development** could be explored with the help of a local environment group or the national 'Council for Environmental Education'. What is the local council Agenda 21?

THE CLOTHES SHOW

GROUP SIZE AND ORGANIZATION
Whole class, then groups.
DURATION
60 minutes.
LEARNING OBJECTIVES
To understand how appropriate clothes can protect health.

YOU WILL NEED

The 'Let's get healthy' poster. Pictures of many different types of clothes from catalogues, and so on. Metal cans, thermometers, hot (but not too hot!) water, pots, spoons, elastic bands, a variety of squares of different materials from old quilts, macs, T-shirts, jeans and track suits, to wrap round the cans.

SENSITIVITIES

Sports clothes are often expensive. Perhaps key items could be hired as children grow out of them so quickly.

WHAT TO DO

Ask the children to look again at the poster, this time concentrating upon what people are wearing.

◆ *Can you see any 'protective' clothing?* (Gardening gloves, sun hat, running shoes, cycle helmet, knee and elbow guards on skateboarder.)

◆ *Why is it important to think about what to wear and how to wear it before doing an activity?*

◆ *What sorts of materials are used in protective clothing?* (Tough, waterproof, insulating, and so on.)

◆ *How could we test these materials to find out how efficient they are at keeping someone warm and dry?*

Discuss the class suggestions and ask groups to organize themselves to set up an investigation to test all or some of the following: the insulating properties of various materials, for instance, cotton, jersey, fleece, etc [a]; the effect of rain upon the insulating power of cotton (for example, jeans) [b]; the insulating power of wet cotton plus a wind [c]; and the waterproof qualities of various materials [d].

Ask the groups to present their results to the class, explaining any of the scientific principles involved they can, (for example, the affect on the body temperature of someone caught in rain and wind without waterproof clothing due to the cooling effect of evaporation, and so on), and to say how their findings will affect their choice of clothes in the future.

INSULATION EXPERIMENTS
(equal volumes of hot water)

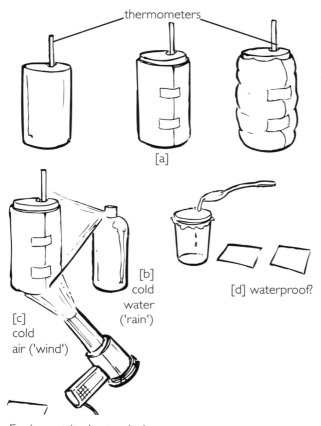

thermometers

[a]

[b] cold water ('rain')

[c] cold air ('wind')

[d] waterproof?

Explore attitudes to clothes:
◆ *Do 'trendy' clothes protect health?*
◆ *How far does 'image' affect choice of clothes?*
◆ *Why is the boy on his bicycle not wearing his helmet correctly?*
◆ *Does he think he will look 'silly' and be jeered at by his friends if he does?*
◆ *What should we say to people wearing protective clothing?* ('Get a lid – get a life!')

Ask each child to select a clothes picture and to write about how the clothes shown protect health. This can be completed in class or as homework.

ASSESSMENT
Do the children seem aware of the importance of protective clothing, and of wearing it correctly?

IDEAS FOR DIFFERENTIATION
For the insulation experiments less able children could feel the cans (check that they are safe to handle) and record which material kept them hot for the longest time. More able children could record the temperature on a graph at, say, five minute intervals (if possible using a sensor linked to a computer).

Less able children could work in pairs and discuss the use of the clothes in the pictures. Others could add scientific comments on the qualities of the materials used in some of the outfits.

EXTENSION WORK
Get children to encourage each other to wear fluorescent and reflective items, safety helmets and so on. The importance of wearing light or reflective clothing on dark winter days could be investigated as part of a topic on 'light and sound'.

This work can be linked with testing the properties of materials against various forces.

DON'T BE A PUSHOVER!

GROUP SIZE AND ORGANIZATION
Whole class, then in groups of three, finally whole class.
DURATION
About 45 minutes.
LEARNING OBJECTIVES
To develop skills for resisting pressures to act in unhealthy ways. To know who to go to for help.

YOU WILL NEED
An enlarged copy of the group in front of the tip on the 'Let's get healthy' poster, plastic cups for one third of the class, water, a timer with a loud bell (kitchen type), flip chart and marker pen or chalkboard and chalk, four sheets of flip chart paper fastened to the wall and headed: *As a persuader I felt...*, *As a resister I felt...*, *As an observer I felt...*, and *What I have learned is...*

SENSITIVITIES
Before this lesson make sure that all children know who in the school they can go to for help, in confidence, if they feel they are being pressured or bullied in any way. There is a fine boundary between 'pressure' and bullying. Negotiate ground rules for working to include that no personal stories are required, and things can be discussed in your class by

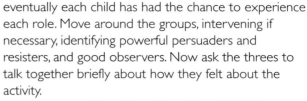

using the people on the poster. This activity can be used to link with drug, alcohol, and anti-smoking education and anti-bullying programmes.

WHAT TO DO
Ask the class to look closely at the children in the enlarged group:
◆ *Can anyone suggest what is going on?*
◆ *What can we deduce from the way the children look (their 'body language')?* (The older children are pressurizing the younger ones to try something they have doubts about.)
◆ *What might they be asking them to do?* (List suggestions on the flip chart.)
◆ *What should the younger children do in this situation?* (Just say 'no', run away, go and tell an adult?)
◆ *Who could they go to for help and advice?* (List these people on another sheet.)
◆ *What might the children be feeling?*

Suggest that it is not always older children who pressurize us to try things that we don't want to do or are that are not good for us: it can be friends of the same age, or even some adults. We all need to develop our skills in resisting such pressures and we can learn how to do this, and practise these skills. Check that the children understand the terms 'persuade' and 'resist'.

Do have a drink! Ask the children to work in threes: as a persuader, a resister and an observer. Give each group a cup of water. List clearly for the observer to refer to during the activity:
Body language: How is each of the pair sitting – persuader leaning forward, resister leaning back?
Eye contact: Who tries to get who to look at them? What facial expressions are used?
Voice: What tone and loudness of voice is used? (Soft and 'persuasive'?, firm?, determined?, weak?, hesitant?)
◆ What key words and phrases are said? (for example, *I won't be your friend if ...?* or *No, I've made up my mind.*)
◆ Who seems most confident?

The persuader is going to try for three minutes to force the resister to accept the drink of water (or any other drink they pretend it is). The resister has to try not to be persuaded. The observer is asked to watch, and to try to analyse what happens. Give them a few moments to think about their role and then start them off with the timer. After three minutes, pause for reflection and then change the roles for another three minutes so that

eventually each child has had the chance to experience each role. Move around the groups, intervening if necessary, identifying powerful persuaders and resisters, and good observers. Now ask the threes to talk together briefly about how they felt about the activity.
◆ *What can we learn from doing this activity?* (Some people are very good at persuading, and it can be very tempting to 'give in', if just to get rid of them!)
◆ *Did anyone think of actually moving away?*
◆ *What were the arguments used by the persuaders?* List these on the flip chart.
◆ *Were some people good at resisting the arguments? Did the persuaders feel that they were really firm?*
◆ *What did these resisters say or do?* These phrases (or behaviour) can be listed on another sheet.

Important: now 'de-role' everybody, asking them to say who they really are, and to relate one nice thing that happened to them last week.

Ask the children to reflect upon what they felt like during this session, and when they are ready, to move around the classroom writing their comments on the wall sheets under any or all of the four headings.

Finish by explaining that we will all be able to use their comments in future sessions when further skills will be identified and practised. All the lists of pressure situations, helpful people, arguments and counter arguments can be added to at any time by anyone.

ASSESSMENT
This activity will enable you to identify children who may be easily influenced by others and who may need support and help in increasing their confidence and assertiveness. How good were the observers in analysing what was going on?

IDEAS FOR DIFFERENTIATION
More able children might draw a series of cartoons showing their 'pressured' role play situation and how it was resolved. Less able children could draw a person saying 'no' to a persuader, or walking away from one.

EXTENSION WORK
Children could collect examples of 'persuaders' and 'resisters' from TV soaps or comics, including ones where the persuaders were getting people to do healthy things, thus extending the ideas to negative and positive pressures.

THE HUMAN LIFE CYCLE

Note: This work should be linked with the school's sex and relationship education policy. Before starting this section you may like to give some thought to whether you would like to ask the school nurse or another health professional to join you for these lessons, and whether it might be appropriate to do some of the work with boys and girls on their own. Some children and parents may prefer this. If you are uncertain about any questions arising from the work, you might like to say something like: 'I'm not sure of the best way to answer that for you. I'll find out and talk to you about it next time'. This will give you the chance to consult with colleagues or health professionals.

WHERE ARE WE NOW?

GROUP SIZE AND ORGANIZATION
Whole class, then pairs, then fours, then whole class.
DURATION
60 minutes.
LEARNING OBJECTIVES
To identify the main stages in the human life cycle.
To look back to establish how far they have come.
To explore concepts of coping with change.

YOU WILL NEED
The 'Let's get healthy' poster, to be used both sides, A4 paper for each pair, two large sheets of paper headed '*The first day at school*', and '*How we feel now*', Questions Box, with slips of paper for everyone.

SENSITIVITIES
You will need to be aware of recent family bereavements or separations where children may need extra support during this session.

WHAT TO DO
Looking at the coloured side of the poster, ask:
◆ *Are all the people the same age?* (No.)
◆ *Who is the youngest?* (The unborn child.)
◆ *Who is the oldest?* (Mrs Wilson, Flat 2.)
Suggest that they both have health needs, and between these two stages, as people grow up, they can take more responsibility for their own health.

Turn over the poster to show the detailed 'Human life cycle': starting with birth, discuss each main stage briefly.
Inner circle: Birth, pre-school, starting school, changing from a child to an adult (called 'puberty', 'adolescence'), leaving school, choice of lifestyle and of special friends:

singles or partnerships, male-female, female-female, male-male, marriages, choice of starting a family.
Outer circle: Round again, as a 'grown up', helpers or workers, gradually ageing, retirement, and ultimately death. (But hopefully we all have a lot of healthy living to do before then!)

Next, turn over the poster and suggest that Mrs Edith Wilson in Flat 2 has recently lost her husband. He died, aged 86, after a long illness.
◆ *How do you think Mrs Wilson must be feeling?* (Sad, lonely, upset, angry, confused, depressed.)
◆ *What could people do to help and support her and her family?* (Listen to her memories, talk with her, sympathize, be with her, send her cards, offer practical help with cooking and shopping, take her flowers – as shown). It will take her some time to become used to her new situation.

Turn the poster back to the life cycle. Point out that people are helping each other along the way.
◆ *Are there any other stages in the life cycle when people might need extra help?* (Pregnancy, at and after a birth, starting school, puberty, changing schools, leaving school... – these can be underlined in colour.)

Working in pairs, focus attention upon the twins, Carli and Tom, when they started school, and ask:
◆ *Do you think Carli and Tom felt exactly the same about starting school?*
◆ *How might Tom have felt? How might Carli have felt?*

Ask the pairs to join into fours and compare their ideas. Which feelings are the same? One person from each four should write down what they think are the most important feelings on the large sheet headed '*A first day at school*'.

Consider what has been written with the whole class. Are there any differences in what girls and boys might feel? Write a summary of the feelings. (Excited, uncertain, insecure, and so on.)

Now ask the class to 'brainstorm' how they now feel about school, and write these words on the second large sheet. Discuss and summarize as before. Compare the two sets of feelings. What do these show us? (Hopefully that although everyone has anxieties, they can be helped to cope with these situations and feelings.)

Refer to the 'Human life cycle' poster and ask a volunteer to identify where the class is now – just before puberty. Suggest that this next stage also involves changes, both physical and emotional, and that these will be explored in the next lesson, together with what help is available. Tell them that if they have any questions or comments they can put them in the Questions Box (anonymously if they wish) and these will be answered during the next lessons.

THE HUMAN LIFE CYCLE

ASSESSMENT

How well are children able to express their emotions about a new situation? Do they understand that everyone has some anxieties, but that they can be helped to cope with them? Are there any gender differences in perception and expression of anxieties? Do the boys or the girls need further help in being able to express uncertainties?

IDEAS FOR DIFFERENTIATION

Pair less able children with more able and encourage them to write down, or draw about, one emotion. The more able could use as many words as possible and develop a role play of a child arriving at the school door, with an adult, on their first day.

EXTENSION WORK

Some children could write an illustrated story about 'My first day at school', or other major change such as moving house. Others could research and make an ongoing display of different stages in the life cycle as depicted by artists. (Mary Cassat's babies and children, Van Gogh's 'First steps', Rembrandt's 'Self portrait' as an old man, and so on.) Others could paint or draw how they think they will look in five, ten and 20 years time. Poems and writing such as Shakespeare's 'Seven ages of man' (Act II, Scene 7 of *As You Like It*) could be acted out at an assembly. Some children might want to explore particular phases – being young, a change in the family, or feelings of bereavement. They might write about the emotions of a friend whose pet has died (or

had to be 'put down'), and who helped them and how. Funeral ceremonies and memorial services in different cultures could be compared, as could marriage and birth celebrations and other acknowledgements of major changes in our life cycles. Children could construct a 'life line', uncurling the stages of the life cycle into a linear format.

LOOKING AHEAD

GROUP SIZE AND ORGANIZATION
Whole class, small groups, then whole class.
DURATION
At least 60 minutes, or you might like to have 2 lessons of 40 minutes.
LEARNING OBJECTIVES
To understand physical and emotional changes at puberty. To develop a vocabulary for communication about sexual matters.

YOU WILL NEED

The 'Let's get healthy' poster, photocopiable pages 27, 28 and 29, wallpaper rolls or large sheets of paper for drawing body outlines, marker pens, copies of pages 28 and 29 made into OHTs (with an OHP) or enlarged sufficiently for class use.

SENSITIVITIES

Children may be apprehensive about discussing sexual changes, so remind the class of the agreed ground rules: no personal questions or teasing. Some giggling is inevitable – explain that this is because we don't often discuss these things in public, but it is important to learn how to talk about our bodies in a sensible way. Early developers (usually girls) may need extra support. All girls should know where to go in school to obtain sanitary towels, in confidence.

WHAT TO DO

Using the 'Let's get healthy' poster, suggest that although our bodies change throughout our lives, the greatest changes for everyone happen when they turn from being a child to being an adult, and become able to reproduce, if they wish. These are **pubertal** changes – write this on the board. (It comes from the Latin word *pubertas*, meaning 'grown up'.) These changes are not just the physical ones, which we have no choice about, but also feelings and relationships with family and friends, and about coping with new opportunities and responsibilities.

BODY PARTS (MALE AND FEMALE)

(for activity on page 22)

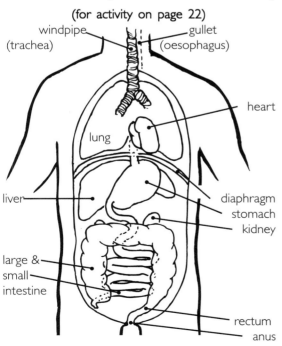

windpipe (trachea)
gullet (oesophagus)
heart
lung
liver
diaphragm
stomach
kidney
large & small intestine
rectum
anus

THE HUMAN LIFE CYCLE

Explain that children all change at different rates which cannot be hurried up or slowed down; they start and finish at different times, and end up different shapes and sizes – as we saw in 'Everybody can do something' (see page 6). The changes take place over several years, so we do have time to get used to them. Ask:

◆ *Can you pick out the people on the poster who have finished their pubertal changes?* (All the adults, parents and passers-by.)
◆ *Can you pick out the children who have not yet started puberty?* (Babies, toddlers, Matt and Emma in Flat 6, and Holly in Flat 1.)
◆ *Which children might be about to start their changes?* (The twins, Tom and Carli, Flat 4, who are now 10½ years old.)

Working in small groups, ask the children to draw round each other to make two body outlines and label one 'Carli', and the other 'Tom'. Now give each child photocopiable page 27 'All change please!'. Read through the story with the class, and ask them to discuss in their groups the list of changes, deciding which would happen to Carli and which to Tom. Tell them to write these by the appropriate outlines and add any feelings that Carli and Tom might have about these changes. Move round the groups, giving extra explanations if necessary.

Go over the answers with the class, discussing the emotions involved and the social consequences – for example, people may treat you more like an adult when your face changes. Ask:

◆ *Why do you think that two of the listed changes had asterisks/stars beside them?* (Because when our bodies start to make sperm or egg cells, we are then **fertile** and capable of becoming parents.)
◆ *How do people know when this has happened?* (When a girl has her first 'period', and a boy has his first 'wet dream' this means that they are then fertile.)

Then ask them to pencil in all the inside organs which are the same for both (see diagram on page 21),

MALE GENITALS

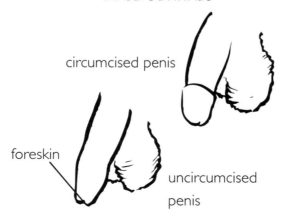

circumcised penis

foreskin

uncircumcised penis

and then those which make a male different from a female – ie, the sex organs inside and outside (**genitals**). The illustrations in this section give further details, *if* required. Move around the groups assessing their vocabulary and understanding.

If time allows and the class is still interested, or in a later session, explain that the twins' Mum did some drawings to help them understand the changes. Give out photocopiable pages 28 and 29. Using the OHTs/ enlarged versions, explain and discuss the pictures and diagrams with the class, referring to Carli and Tom. Ask the groups to discuss each page and if they would like to change any anatomical details on their outline drawings (or add any 'correct' words). This might be a good point to highlight the use of sanitary towels.

Each time finish the lesson with reassurance that:
◆ everyone has their own timescale for puberty – some start earlier than others. (Film star Nicole Kidman was 5' 10", 1.8m, when she was 13, and 'felt like an "alien"'! Churchill, on the other hand, was a late developer.) Girls can start between 8 and 17, boys between 10 and 18.
◆ there will be help for coping with changes at any time if anyone wants it. (The school nurse might be willing to talk to individuals.) The Questions Box is always available for enquiries.

ASSESSMENT
How much correct information did the children have about pubertal changes? Were they able to discuss them sensibly and use new words appropriately? These skills can be developed further over the next sessions.

IDEAS FOR DIFFERENTIATION
Cut up copies of photocopiable pages 28 and 29 into individual pictures and ask the less able children to arrange them in sequence. They could tell you three ways in which girls differ from boys, and three ways in which boys and girls change as they grow up. More able children can begin to compile a glossary of the scientific terms used, for themselves and for the class.

EXTENSION WORK
Children could write a list of questions to ask the school nurse, and invite her/him in to discuss the answers. Some could write a letter to a friend explaining pubertal changes. Others could act as agony aunts and uncles, and answer questions from girls' groups and boys' groups, either in writing to be displayed, or verbally in a 'chat show' mode. This work could be linked with 'safe' and 'not safe' touches, and which parts of the body are appropriately touched by which people.

THE HUMAN LIFE CYCLE

IN THE BEGINNING

GROUP SIZE AND ORGANIZATION
Whole class, small groups then whole class.
DURATION
45 minutes.
LEARNING OBJECTIVES
To learn about conception. To understand the choice of family planning. To consider the expectations of family members.

YOU WILL NEED
The 'Let's get healthy' poster, and a copy of photocopiable page 30 for each child.

SENSITIVITIES
While discussing the value of planning to have a baby, it is important not to imply that any unplanned babies might be unwanted. Children should understand that adopted children are born in the same way as others, but because of great difficulties their birth mothers reluctantly decide they would have a better life being looked after by another family.

WHAT TO DO
Ask the class to look at the colour side of the poster and focus attention upon the family in Flat 1, Mrs Ann Tyler, her 3 year old daughter Holly, and the midwife coming to the door.
◆ *Why do you think the midwife is calling on Mrs Tyler?* (Because Mrs Tyler is pregnant, and midwives help mothers look after themselves and their unborn babies.)
◆ *What is the midwife going to do?* (Examine Mrs Tyler, ask her how she's feeling, listen to the baby's heartbeat, check the probable time of birth and what arrangements have been made to look after Holly.)
◆ *Where else might Mrs Tyler have obtained help?* (From an antenatal – before birth – clinic where many mothers and fathers go to prepare.)

Suggest that the family, grandparents, uncles, and aunts are greatly looking forward to meeting the new family member – but how did the baby start? Explain that it takes a man and a woman together to make a baby – a rather amazing process!

Working in groups, give each child photocopiable page 30 and help them follow the story. During this time you can explain sexual intercourse in your own words or say something like (the words in bold could be written on the board): 'When a man and a woman love each other, they hug and kiss in a special way we call making love, or **sexual intercourse**. The woman's **vagina** becomes wet and slippery, and the man's **penis** becomes stiff (an **erection**) and he can slide his penis into her vagina. This gives the couple great pleasure and leads to a **climax** (orgasm or 'come') when **sperm**

FEMALE SEXUAL ORGANS – INTERNAL & EXTERNAL VIEWS

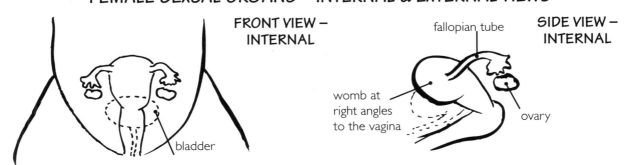

FRONT VIEW – INTERNAL

bladder

SIDE VIEW – INTERNAL

fallopian tube

womb at right angles to the vagina

ovary

FRONT VIEW – EXTERNAL

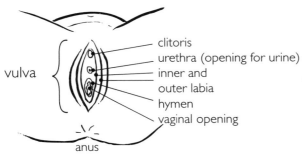

vulva

clitoris
urethra (opening for urine)
inner and outer labia
hymen
vaginal opening

anus

(Please note that these diagrams are for your information only. It is not intended that this level of detail should necessarily be shared with the children.)

in a little liquid called **semen** spurt out of the penis into the vagina. The millions of sperm swim up the **cervix**, through the **womb** and into the **fallopian tubes**. If they meet an **egg cell**, one of the sperm pushes into it, and the egg is now **fertilized**. After making love the couple feel relaxed and the penis and vagina go back to normal.'

As you go around the groups, ask them to think about the Tyler family on the bottom of photocopiable page 30. What do you think that Mrs Tyler, Mr Tyler, Holly and the unborn baby are feeling?

Now refer the whole class back to the poster and the young couple Janice and Mark in Flat 3. Suggest that although they like children very much, they do not want to have any themselves at the moment.

◆ *Why do you think they may have decided this?* (Too much responsibility, not enough money, both working long hours, or out of work, want to wait until they are older, and so on.) Agree that these are all good reasons, but in the meantime they do love one another and want to 'make love', but not start a baby.

◆ *Does anyone know what they might choose to do to stop a sperm joining with an egg cell?* Some children will have heard of 'the pill', so elaborate by explaining that a doctor can prescribe a woman this medicine to take every day to stop her ovaries releasing egg cells.

Condoms can be explained as a very thin rubber sheath or bag which can be rolled over a man's erect penis, to catch the sperm so that they cannot join with an egg cell.

Condoms are also used to protect people from catching certain sex-related infections (such as the HIV virus which can and condoms are types of contraceptive (the word comes from *contra*, Latin for against, and (con)*ception*). They help people to enjoy 'sexual health'.

Ask the children:

◆ *Do you think the decision to have a baby or not is important?*

◆ *Do you think couples should talk to each other about if and when they should have a baby?*

◆ *When do you think is the best time to have a baby?*

End with a reminder that as soon as a girl is fertile (has her first period) or a boy is fertile (has his first wet dream), they could become parents if they have sexual intercourse. People who are

fertile have a tremendous responsibility. Nobody has to have sex if they don't want to. Remind the children about resisting 'persuaders' (see page 19).

ASSESSMENT

Ask the class to reflect upon what new things they have learned, how they feel about all this and what they would like to know more about. Use the children's discussion and questions in order to assess their level of understanding and their attitudes. You may need to go back over some of the detail and explore the emotional and relationship aspects more fully.

IDEAS FOR DIFFERENTIATION

Less able children could be asked to focus upon the Tyler family on the photocopiable page 30, to colour in the picture and write as many words as they can about them. Able children can answer the quiz and make up some more questions and answers, or a crossword puzzle, using the information on the sheet.

BABY IN THE WOMB (40 WEEKS)

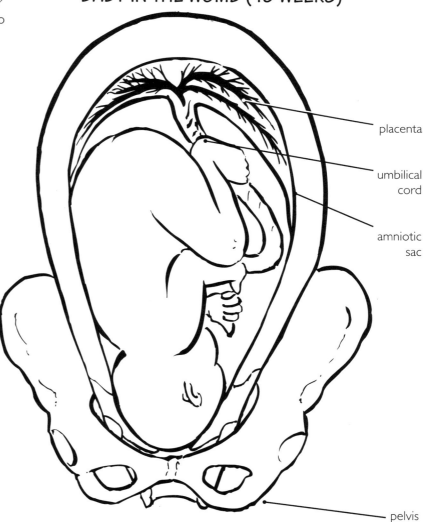

placenta

umbilical cord

amniotic sac

pelvis

THE HUMAN LIFE CYCLE

EXTENSION WORK

The class could discuss what questions they would like to ask a midwife or antenatal nurse, who could be invited to visit. A pregnant mum (with partner?) might be willing to have her progress, feelings and the size of the bump measured and recorded by the class. You might like to explain more about foetal development and the functions of the placenta, umbilical cord and membranes before the next lesson.

PREPARING FOR THE NEW ARRIVAL

GROUP SIZE AND ORGANIZATION
Whole class, small groups, then whole class.
DURATION
45 minutes.
LEARNING OBJECTIVES
To understand the birth process. To explore the responsibilities of parents.

YOU WILL NEED

For each child: a copy of photocopiable page 31 'The new arrival'. For each group: one extra copy of photocopiable page 31, glue sticks, cut-out pictures from magazines and leaflets of varied ethnic groups of pregnant women, babies, mothers and fathers with newborn or older babies, and of baby equipment. For class use: three large sheets of paper headed 'Being a parent means:', 'The advantages of being a parent are:', and 'The disadvantages of being a parent are:'.

SENSITIVITIES

Acknowledge that birth experiences can be varied, but reassure children that a great deal of help is available during antenatal care and the birth itself. Girls, in particular, may have worries due to negative information from anecdotes, TV and media coverage of exceptional cases. Children being looked after by people other than their own parents may need extra support during this lesson.

WHAT TO DO

Remind the class that the Tyler family baby is due very soon. Tell them that babies don't always keep exactly to the 40 weeks **gestation** (time spent growing inside their mothers). They can be born slightly earlier or slightly later. Ask:
◆ *Does anyone know how a mother knows when a baby is near to being born?*
(She feels 'contractions', a strong pulling feeling as the muscles of the womb contract to open the cervix wide enough to let the baby out. This can take place over some hours and is followed by an urge to push the baby out. The thin bag of fluid round the baby may break, so a gush of 'water' may be a sign that labour – hard work! – is starting.)

Explain that we are going to find out what happened when the Tyler baby decided it would be 'delivery day'!

Working in groups, distribute photocopiable page 31 and read through the story sequence with the children. (They can decide whether the baby is a boy or girl.) While they are answering the questions or colouring the sheet, move around the groups answering questions: 'Yes, giving birth can be painful, but pain relief is given', 'Yes, some mothers can choose

THE HUMAN LIFE CYCLE

to give birth in the position most comfortable for them', 'No, it does not hurt when the umbilical cord is cut as there are no nerves in it', 'The **placenta** is passed out as the **afterbirth** as it is no longer needed' and 'Yes, the vast majority of the almost six billion people on the earth have been born in this way'. (The other is by Caesarian section which the children may have heard about.)

Now ask the groups to arrange the cut-out pictures in sequence, before and after a birth, and to stick these onto the large sheet together with the equipment needed – nappies, clothes, cot, and so on (which can be costed from catalogues).

They might like to cut up an extra copy of photocopiable page 31 and stick the pictures in the appropriate place in sequence. Ask them while they are doing this to discuss what parents have to do to keep their babies safe, well and happy, before and after birth. The completed sheets can be displayed and compared.

Finally, with the whole class, consider the questions on the large sheets and collect their ideas about 'Being a parent means:', 'The advantages of being a parent are:', and 'The disadvantages of being a parent are:'.

ASSESSMENT
Ask the class to reflect upon what they have learned:
◆ *What do you think was the most interesting part?*
◆ *What was the least interesting part?*
◆ *What would you like to know more about?*
You will need to consider:
◆ How well are the children able to describe the birth process, both in scientific and emotional terms?
◆ How far do they understand the practical and emotional responsibilities of parenthood? Are they able to communicate in a sensible way, without embarrassment, using a 'correct' vocabulary? Are they able to formulate questions appropriately?

IDEAS FOR DIFFERENTIATION
During group work, less able children could start sorting out the pictures at once, and select four items of equipment to illustrate needs. More able children could list and cost all basic equipment and estimate a total minimum sum, allowing for second hand items (and presents!).

EXTENSION WORK
Some children could research the overall cost of having a child, taking into account any loss of the mother's earnings, maternity allowances and leave. Some could do a survey of birth congratulations cards, decide if they were sexist or not, and design 'equal opportunities' ones. Others could investigate the pink/blue syndrome by assessing catalogues of children's clothes and toys for stereotypical images. Parents of young babies might be willing to bring them along to let the children see them being bathed and changed, and to experience how little the babies can do for themselves. Children could make a child development chart and visit a nursery or crèche to collect information on different age groups. Parenting skills could be investigated – listening, helping, playing with, teaching, and so on, and practised with children from younger classes.

RESOURCE
BANK

HEALTHY LIVING

THE HUMAN LIFE CYCLE

Name ————————————— Date —————————————

All change please!

The ten year-old twins, Tom and Carli, were helping their Mum to sort out clothes for a weekend stay with their cousins. They had matching tracksuits and anoraks. "But Mum, they're too small for me!" said Carli, showing how her arms and legs stuck out of them. "I'm taller than Tom."

"You can't be," said Tom, "we've always been the same size."

"We can soon measure that," said Mum, and sure enough Carli was a good 2cm taller than her brother. "Ah," said Mum, "I think you must be starting your pubertal growth spurt, Carli. Girls often do start before boys."

Carli felt rather pleased, but also a little anxious. What was going to happen to her?

Tom felt jealous. When would he start growing and need new clothes? He hoped he wasn't going to be asked to wear Carli's old tracksuit!

◆ Here is a list of 20 changes that will happen to Carli and Tom. Can you sort out which will happen to Carli and which to Tom? (Helpful hints: some changes happen to both boys and girls, and 'quickly' means over about a year or so).

1. Feet, legs, arms and hands grow quickly.
2. Growth in height quickly.
3. Breasts and nipples grow.
4. Skin and hair become more oily.
5. Sweat glands make more sweat.
6. Hair grows between the legs (pubic hair).
7. Testicles begin to make sperm*.
8. Hair grows on the face, starting with the upper lip.
9. Hips grow wider and a waist develops, resulting in a more 'rounded' shape.
10. Wet dreams start.
11. Ovaries grow and begin to release egg cells, one per month*.
12. Shoulders grow wider and hips (relatively) narrower.
13. Testicles and penis grow.
14. Periods start (about two years after breasts start to grow).
15. Voice becomes much deeper.
16. Mood swings happen.
17. Face changes from 'baby' to more adult.
18. May get spots.
19. Increase in strength of muscles.
20. Feelings about sex change.

PHOTOCOPIABLE
RESOURCE
BANK

THE HUMAN LIFE CYCLE

Name _____   Date _____

Girls growing up

The outside story
How old do you think these girls are?

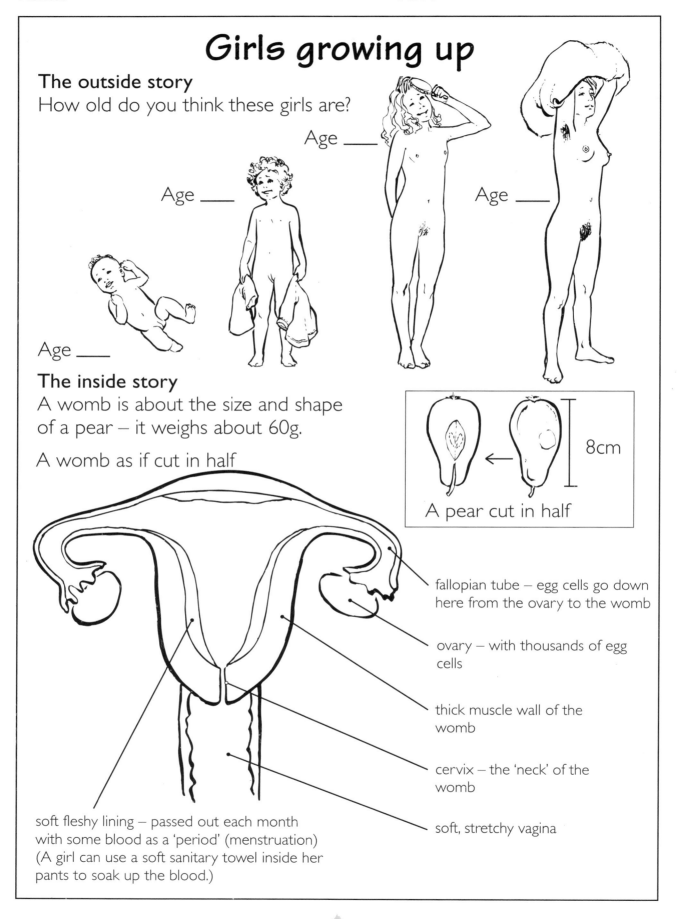

Age ____

Age ____

Age ____

Age ____

The inside story
A womb is about the size and shape of a pear – it weighs about 60g.

A womb as if cut in half

8cm

A pear cut in half

fallopian tube – egg cells go down here from the ovary to the womb

ovary – with thousands of egg cells

thick muscle wall of the womb

cervix – the 'neck' of the womb

soft, stretchy vagina

soft fleshy lining – passed out each month with some blood as a 'period' (menstruation) (A girl can use a soft sanitary towel inside her pants to soak up the blood.)

THE HUMAN LIFE CYCLE

Name _____ Date _____

Boys growing up

The outside story

How old do you think these boys are?
Which one may have just started
puberty?

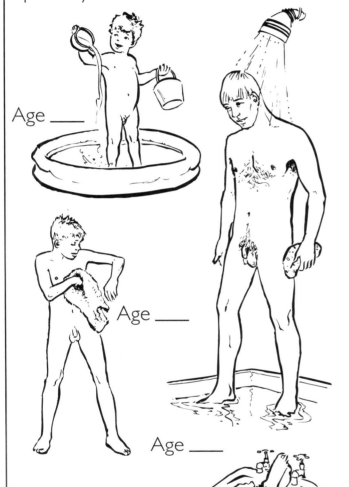

Age ____

Age ____

Age ____

Age ____

The inside story

At puberty a boy's testicles
begin to make sperm.
Sperm are so small that they
can only be seen using a
microscope.
Each testicle makes 2,000
sperm per second – about 200
million per day!
They leave the body through
the penis, in a teaspoonful of
fluid called semen when a boy
has a 'wet dream' and
ejaculates ('comes').
Urine and semen never come
out together.
Can you trace the path of the
sperm?

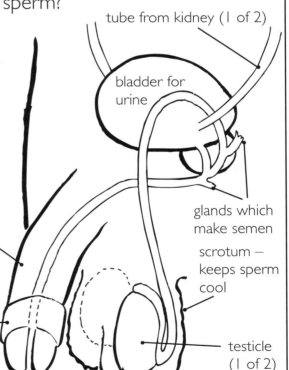

tube from kidney (1 of 2)

bladder for
urine

glands which
make semen

scrotum –
keeps sperm
cool

penis

testicle
(1 of 2)

foreskin – some
boys have this
removed (called
circumcision)

PHOTOCOPIABLE
RESOURCE
BANK

THE HUMAN LIFE CYCLE

Name _____   Date _____

Just beginning

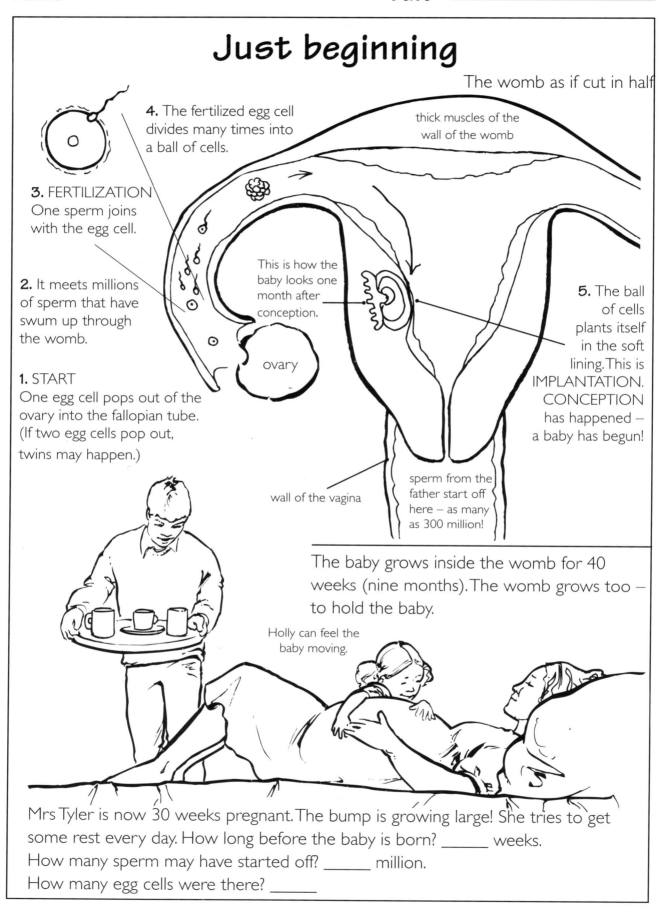

The womb as if cut in half

4. The fertilized egg cell divides many times into a ball of cells.

thick muscles of the wall of the womb

3. FERTILIZATION
One sperm joins with the egg cell.

2. It meets millions of sperm that have swum up through the womb.

This is how the baby looks one month after conception.

ovary

1. START
One egg cell pops out of the ovary into the fallopian tube. (If two egg cells pop out, twins may happen.)

5. The ball of cells plants itself in the soft lining. This is IMPLANTATION. CONCEPTION has happened — a baby has begun!

wall of the vagina

sperm from the father start off here — as many as 300 million!

The baby grows inside the womb for 40 weeks (nine months). The womb grows too — to hold the baby.

Holly can feel the baby moving.

Mrs Tyler is now 30 weeks pregnant. The bump is growing large! She tries to get some rest every day. How long before the baby is born? _____ weeks.
How many sperm may have started off? _____ million.
How many egg cells were there? _____

PHOTOCOPIABLE
RESOURCE BANK

THE HUMAN LIFE CYCLE

Name _____   Date _____

The new arrival

The baby has been growing inside Mrs Ann Tyler for _____ weeks. Mr Brian Tyler has been helping with the chores.

The baby has been happy inside; in its warm 'swimming pool', sucking its thumb and listening to its mummy's heartbeat.

But now it's getting a bit squashed! Time to come out!

Mrs Tyler can feel a strong 'pulling' – contractions of her womb.
Time to get some help.
Holly goes to Mrs Wilson's.

Brian drives Ann to the hospital.

The midwife welcomes them and helps.

One more push!
Holly meets her new _____
What do you think Holly is feeling?

The baby is washed, weighed and measured.

The cord is clamped, and will dry up and drop off. It leaves a mark called a _____
Have we all got one of these? _____

HEALTHY LIVING

PHOTOCOPIABLE
RESOURCE
BANK

HEALTHY LIVING REVIEW

THE FLAT 5 FAMILY

GROUP SIZE AND ORGANIZATION
Whole class, small groups, then whole class.
DURATION
60 minutes.
LEARNING OBJECTIVES
To understand what is meant by a 'healthy lifestyle'.
To revise key points from previous sections.
To evaluate the 'Healthy Living' lessons.

YOU WILL NEED
The 'Let's get healthy' poster, a large sheet of paper and pens for each group.
In advance, write up on the flip chart, board or OHP:
Flat 5 is a three-bedroomed flat, available for rent.
In your group, discuss and report on one of the families who have come to look around the flat.
On your sheet, describe and draw the family.
◆ What is their name? Do they have any children? What are their ages? Do they believe in 'good health'? What sort of lifestyle do they have at the moment?
Discuss and decide:
◆ What sort of food do they eat?
◆ How do they exercise?
◆ How do they keep themselves clean?
◆ How do they keep themselves safe?
◆ What are their likes and dislikes?
◆ How would they be good neighbours?

SENSITIVITIES
Try to encourage the children to portray a variety of families, rather than an unrealistic, 'perfect health' model.

WHAT TO DO
With the whole class, look at the poster and ask:
◆ What have we learned about the health of the families in the flats? (In Flat 6, the Adams grow vegetables, and Michael now gets enough sleep. In Flat 4 the twins are reassured about puberty. In Flat 3 Janice and Mark have decided to postpone parenthood. In Flat 2 a depressed Mrs Wilson has been supported by her neighbours. In Flat 1 the Tyler family now have a new baby. All the families co-operated to write to and meet the local councillor in order to get action on the tip.)
◆ Do you think they all have a healthy lifestyle?
Discuss what a 'lifestyle' means, and ask for some examples. Suggest that lifestyles can change.
◆ How do you think having a baby has changed the lifestyle of the Tyler family?
Now focus attention upon Flat 5: who lives there? (Nobody at the moment, but the 'Flat to rent' sign shows that it is available.) Explain that each group is going to invent a family who might be coming to view the flat. Ask them to follow the guidelines on the flip chart or OHP to describe their family. Move round the groups helping them to consider as many of the health issues as possible.

Ask the groups to present their 'families' to the class, explaining their reasons for the choice of lifestyle. The family sheets can be displayed and added to later.

ASSESSMENT
This activity will enable you to find out how much the children have understood and retained about the value of a 'healthy lifestyle', and its different components.

Have they developed a vocabulary for communicating about health? Which area may need reinforcing and extending? How have the children assessed the course?
Ask the class to reflect:
◆ Did you enjoy this activity?
◆ What did you learn by doing it?
Finally, thank the children for all their hard work, and either formally (by writing on paper or graffiti sheets) or informally (verbally, by discussion), ask them:
◆ How do you feel about the 'Healthy living' lessons?
◆ What did you like best?
◆ What didn't you like?
◆ What new things did you learn to do?
◆ What did you know about already?
◆ What more would you like to learn about health?

IDEAS FOR DIFFERENTIATION
Within the groups less able children could concentrate upon one family person, and one health aspect; others could describe more elaborate relationships within the family.

EXTENSION WORK
The 'designer family' can be used as the basis for stories, role play or dramas, using the children's own agenda, and thus exploring issues which are important to them. The teaching in Healthy Living should be ongoing and should contribute to an overall healthy school programme, enjoyed by everyone.
Health matters!

RESOURCE BANK